Gran and ...

written by Jay Dale

illustrated by Michelle Dybing

"I am on the ferris wheel," said Carlos.

"Look at Gran and me!"

3

"I am on the boat,"
said Carlos.
"Look at Gran and me!"

5

"I am on the bouncy castle," said Carlos.

"Look at Gran and me!"

"I am on the roller coaster," said Carlos.
"Look at Gran and me!"

"I am on the swing,"
said Carlos.
"Look at Gran and me!"

11

"I am on the train,"
said Carlos.
"Look at Gran and me!"

13

"I am on the merry-go-round," said Carlos.

"Look at Gran and me!"

"Look at Gran and me!"